Helen Crawley

FOOD PORTION SIZES

London: HMSO

CONTENTS

Standard weights and measures

1 ounce	=	28.35g
1 pound	=	453.6g
1 gram	=	0.0353 oz
1 kilogram	=	2.20516 lb

1 fluid ounce	=	28.41 ml
1 pint	=	568.3 ml
1 litre	=	1.76 pints

1 teaspoonful	= $\frac{1}{8}$ fl oz	= about 4 ml
1 dessertspoonful	= $\frac{1}{4}$ fl oz	= about 10 ml
1 tablespoonful	= $\frac{1}{2}$ fl oz	= about 18 ml

INTRODUCTION

This book has been compiled to provide information on typical weights and portion sizes of food eaten in Britain. It provides dietitians, nutritionists, and anyone wishing to estimate how much they eat, with average values for the weights of both individual food items and average portion sizes. By using this book in conjunction with nutritional information on food labels or a standard reference book of food composition such as the Ministry of Agriculture, Fisheries and Food's Manual of Nutrition[1], McCance and Widdowson's 'The Composition of Foods'[2] and its supplements[3] (all of which present nutrient values in 100g of the food), the energy and nutrients in portions of the foods and therefore in a typical day's meals can be calculated.

The information in this book has been collected during a large number of weighed dietary studies carefully conducted by the Ministry of Agriculture, Fisheries and Food throughout Britain. In addition, weights have been taken from manufacturers' information and by weighing numerous items of food, particularly take-away foods and foods which are not yet required by law to be labelled with their weight.

The weights in this book fall into two categories:

1 Weights of specific discrete items eg. a packet of crisps, a chocolate bar, a biscuit, an ice-lolly etc.
2 Average portions of larger items eg of meat pie, vegetables, apple crumble etc.

Individual items
In many cases a specific name or brand is sufficient to distinguish a particular product eg a 'bourbon biscuit', but it is still important to check the weight given on the packet

wherever possible. Weights of manufactured foods may vary as manufacturers increase and decrease weights and prices, or may offer larger packs for promotional purchases. It is important to be aware that all 'standard' weights can vary from those printed here and that there can be significant differences between brands.

Where the information is less specific this book can also be used to obtain a suitable estimate or average value. In such cases, first check the exact food description: apples can be 'small' or 'large', and other foods as purchased can vary from the 'bite size' to the 'economy'. If the packet is not available, an idea of size or purchase price, number of items in a pack or outlet from which it was purchased can all provide useful information. We have tried to include as far as possible the main variations in weight for the same food.

Average portion sizes
Portions from larger items or packets are more variable and this book can at best only provide an estimate of the actual amount consumed. Whilst the values should be reasonably accurate across a population, any individual's intake could be quite different. However, many weights can be made more accurate if more is known about the food eaten, eg half a large tin of baked beans or a full bowl of cornflakes. Users may need to weigh particular foods to familiarise themselves with small, medium and large portions or thick and thin spreadings. It is often more difficult to assign portion sizes to food eaten outside the home but weights of many standard fast foods and ethnic dishes have been included in the appropriate section.

The book is divided into sections alphabetically, and foods are then listed alphabetically within each group. Foods which fit into more than one section may appear twice. There will also inevitably be cases where regional or ethnic dishes appear under names other than the familiar local names.

This is the first edition of what is planned to be a regularly updated booklet, and we would appreciate users' and manufacturers' comments on presentation and on specific weights. We would also welcome suggestions for extending it further.

I would like to thank David Buss, Janet Lewis, Alison Mills, Katrine Sutherland and Anne Wheeler-Clarke for their help and advice in compiling the information in this book.

Helen Crawley
Ministry of Agriculture,
Fisheries and Food
March 1988

This is a reprint of the first edition. Amendments have been made to a few items following users' and manufacturers comments. Since 1988 many new products have been developed and weights of selected items have been incorporated. Those products which are no longer available have been deleted. The main areas of revision are the sections on Milk, cream, ice-cream and yoghurt; Confectionery and Biscuits.

We would like to thank the following manufacturers who were most cooperative with the revision of this booklet: Cadbury Ltd, Lyons Maid Ltd, Birds Eye Walls Ltd and St. Ivel Ltd in addition to Carol Albert and Helen Rose from MAFF.

Nutrition Branch
Ministry of Agriculture,
Fisheries and Food
October 1990

[1] Manual of Nutrition, 9th Edition, MAFF/HMSO, 1985
[2] McCance and Widdowson's 'The Composition of Foods'. A A Paul, D A T Southgate 4th edition. HMSO 1978
[3] Cereals and Cereal Products. B Holland, I D Unwin, D H Buss. RSC/HMSO 1988
[4] Immigrant Foods. S P Tan, R W Wenlock, D H Buss. HMSO 1985
[5] Milk Products and Eggs. B Holland, I D Unwin, D H Buss. RSC/HMSO 1989

BEVERAGES

Alcoholic drinks

Babycham	1 bottle	*100g*
Barley wine	1 bottle	*180g*
Beer/lager	1 pint	*574g*
	½ pint	*287g*
	bottle	*250/300g*
	small can	*333g*
	large can	*444g*
Liqueurs	1 measure	*25g*
Sherry	1 glass, small	*50g*
	large	*100g*
Spirits	1 measure (England and Wales)	*23g*
	(Scotland)	*27g*
	1 airline measure	*48g*
	1 miniature	*29g*
Vermouth	1 measure	*48g*
Wine	1 average glass	*125g*
	1 small bottle	*200g*
	1 half bottle	*375g*
	1 average bottle	*750g*

Soft drinks and fruit juices

Carbonated canned drink	standard can	*330g*
	slim can	*250g*
Fresh orange juice	1 orange, freshly squeezed	*50g*
Fruit juice	average glass	*200g*
	individual carton	*200g*
	tall tumbler	*300g*
	wine glass	*120g*

Beverages

Instant fruit drink powder	to make 1 pint	74g
Lime cordial	in ½ pint lager	45g
	in 1 pint lager	90g
Mixers	average with spirit	110g
Pub bottles juices/mixers		110g
Ribena	concentrate, average measure	60g
	individual carton	250g
Squash	concentrate, average measure	40g
	diluted, per glass	200g
	individual carton	200g

Non-alcoholic drinks

Chocolate break	1 sachet	28g
Cocoa	1 teaspoon heaped	6g
	level	2g
Coffee	1 average cup	190g
	1 average mug	260g
	1 average vending machine cup	170g
	1 teaspoon instant, heaped	2g
	level	1g
Drinking chocolate	for 1 mug	18g
Horlicks/Ovaltine	for 1 mug	24g
	1 sachet	23g
Nesquik	for 1 tumbler of milk	15g
	1 rounded teaspoon	5g
Lemon tea	1 teaspoon instant	2g
	instant for 1 mug	6g
Tea	1 average cup	190g
	1 average mug	260g
	1 average vending machine cup	170g

Beverages

5

BISCUITS

Abbey crunch	*10g*
All butter fruit	*17g*
All butter shortbread	*13g*
All butter thins	*5g*
Almond shortie	*8g*
Animals	*10g*
Arrowroot	*7g*
Assorted Creams	*12g*
Balisto, Mars	*21g*
Bandit	*24g*
Bath Oliver	*15g*
Blue Riband	*29g*
Bourbon	*12g*
Braemar	*10g*
Bran	*22g*
Brandy snaps	*15g*
Breakaway	*21g*
Burford	*13g*
Butter crunch	*7g*
Butter puffs	*10g*
Caramel Wafer (Tunnocks)	*27g*
Cheddars	*4g*
Mini Cheddars	*2g*
Cheese sandwich	*7g*
Cheese thins	*4g*
Choc au lait	*10g*
Chocolate and nut cookies	*11g*
Chocolate chip gingers	*12g*
Chocolate fingers	*6g*
Classic bar, Fox's	*30g*
Club (all except wafer)	*24g*
Club wafer	*19g*
Cluster (all varieties)	*28g*
Coasters	*10g*
Coconut cookies	*15g*
Coconut fingers	*7g*

Coconut mallows		*11g*
Corn crisp, 1/8		*20g*
Cornish creams		*16g*
Cream crackers		*7g*
Crispbread	Crackerbread	*10g*
	extra thin	*5g*
	Kavli	*10g*
	Kavli finger	*5g*
	Primula thin	*5g*
	Ryvita	*10g*
	Scanda	*6g*
	wholemeal	*15g*
Crunchy bars, Jordans		*33g*
Currant crisp		*7g*
Currant crunch cream		*12g*
Custard cream		*12g*

Devon creams		*11g*
Digestive	McVitie's	*17g*
	sweetmeal	*13g*
	chocolate, McVitie's	*17g*
	sweetmeal, chocolate	*13g*
	full coated	*20g*

Farleys rusk	*17g*
Farmhouse crackers	*8g*
Fig rolls	*18g*
Fingers, chocolate coated	*6g*
Fivers	*17g*
French toast	*8g*
Fruit shortcake	*8g*

Garibaldi	*8g*
Ginger crunch creams	*13g*
Ginger nuts	*9g*
Ginger snaps	*7g*
Ginger thins	*7g*
Gipsy creams	*14g*
Gold bar, McVities	*26g*
Golden crumble	*9g*
Golden crunch creams	*13g*

Harvest crunch bars		*20g*
Hi-Lo crackers		*5g*
Hob-nobs	plain	*15g*
	chocolate coated	*17g*
Hob Nob bar, McVities		*28g*
Honey and oatmeal		
cookies		*10g*
Hovis crackers		*7g*
Iced gems		*2g*
Iced sports		*9g*
Jaffa cakes		*12g*
Jam sandwich creams		*13g*
Jamborees		*20g*
Jammy dodgers		*17g*
Jaspers, McVities		*12g*
Jaspers Chocoloate coated,		
McVities		*15g*
Jump cereal bar		*21g*
Kavli	crispbread	*10g*
	crispbread fingers	*5g*
Kracka wheat		*8g*
Krisprolls		*10g*
Lemon crispy creams		*10g*
Lemon puff		*10g*
Lincoln biscuits		*10g*
MacVita		*10g*
Mallows		*12g*
Malt crunch creams		*13g*
Malted milk		*9g*
Malted milk creams		*12g*
Marie		*7g*
Marshmallow teacake		*18g*
Maryland cookies		*9g*
Mini cookies	bag	*45g*
	each	*3g*
Morning coffee		*4g*
Muesli cookies		*13g*

Munchmallow		*18g*
Natural choice	wholemeal digestive	*13g*
	fruit and nut crunch	*10g*
	muesli	*17g*
Nice		*7g*
Oatcakes	round	*13g*
	triangle	*17g*
Oaten crunch		*8g*
Orange creams		*12g*
Original crunch bars		*33g*
Osborne, butter		*8g*
Peanut crunch		*10g*
Penguin		*24g*
Petit beurre		*7g*
Petticoat tails		*13g*
Plain chocolate digestive		*17g*
Plain chocolate **homewheat**		*18g*
Primula thins		*5g*
Raspberry creams		*10g*
Rice cake		*9g*
Rich tea		*7g*
Ritz	plain	*3g*
	cheese sandwich	*8g*
	cheese and onion sandwich	*8g*
Royal Scot		*10g*
Ryvita		*10g*
Scanda		*6g*
Sesame seed cracker		*4g*
Shortbread finger		*15g*
Shortcake		*10g*
Snack		*8g*
Snowballs		*25g*
Sultana cookies		*17g*
Taxi		*14g*
Thin arrowroot		*7g*

Biscuits

Toffypops		18g
Tracker		27g
Treacle crunch creams		13g
Trio		24g
Tuc		5g
Triple bar, Fox's		22g
Twiglets	each	1g
	per packet	50g
Tyrol bar, Prewetts		28g
United		23g
Viennese fingers		21g
Viscount		16g
Wafer, not coated		15g
Wafer, pink filled		7g
Wagon wheels		31g
Water biscuits		8g
Wholemeal	bran	15g
	crispbread	5g
	shortbread	15g
YoYo		19g

Biscuits, if name not specified = averages

Cheese biscuits		4g
Cream sandwich biscuits		12g
Full coated chocolate biscuits		24g
Semi-sweet biscuits	eg marie	7g
Sweet biscuits	cookies, crunch	10g
Wafer biscuits	(cream filled, not ice-cream wafers)	7g

BREAD, ROLLS, CHAPATIS ETC.

Breadstick		*7g*
Brioche	individual	*45g*
Chapati	white or brown, average, without fat	*55g*
	with fat	*60g*
Croissant	chocolate, 'pain-au-chocolat'	*60g*
	plain	*50g*
	savoury filled	*90g*
	mini	*35g*
Croutons	with soup, homemade	*25g*
	purchased	*15g*
Crumpet	toasted	*40g*
Danish style light bread		
sliced	medium slice fresh	*20g*
	toasted	*18g*
French stick	2" slice	*40g*
	6" slice	*120g*
French toast	bread coated in egg, fried, 1 slice	*70g*
Garlic bread	1 slice	*30g*
	restaurant portion	*120g*
Malt loaf	1 slice	*35g*
Muffin	white, toasted	*68g*
	wholemeal, toasted	*72g*
Naan bread		*160g*
Nimble, sliced	1 slice fresh	*20g*
	toasted	*18g*
Papadum	fried	*13g*
	grilled	*10g*

Breads

Paratha	plain	*140g*
	stuffed	*170g*
Piklets	toasted, each	*25g*
Pitta bread	'mini', picnic	*35g*
	small	*75g*
	large	*95g*
Potato cake/bread	1 farl, fried	*60g*
	grilled	*56g*
Pumpernickel	1 average slice	*33g*
Puri, fried		*70g*
Rolls	bagel	*90g*
	bap, granary, white or wholemeal (6″ diameter)	*112g*
	bridge roll	*20g*
	granary roll	*56g*
	hamburger bun bakers	*85g*
	prepacked	*50g*
	hovis, 'mini loaf'	*56g*
	krisp roll eg Pogeus	*10g*
	white roll, crusty	*50g*
	soft	*45g*
	wholemeal roll, crusty	*48g*
	soft	*43g*
Roti, bread	cooked in tandoor	*100g*
Rye bread	1 average slice	*25g*
Slimcea, sliced,	1 slice fresh	*15g*
	toasted	*13g*
Soda bread	1 farl	*130g*
Staffordshire oatcake		*50g*
Toasting loaf	white, 1 slice fresh	*30g*
	toasted	*27g*

White crusty bread	small loaf, 1 slice fresh	27g
	toasted	24g
	large loaf 1 medium slice fresh	35g
	toasted	31g
	large loaf, 1 thick slice fresh	50g
	toasted	45g
White sliced bread	small loaf, 1 slice fresh	23g
	toasted	20g
	large loaf 1 thin slice fresh	25g
	toasted	22g
	large loaf, 1 medium slice fresh	30g
	toasted	27g
	large loaf, 1 thick slice fresh	38g
	toasted	34g
Wholemeal sliced bread	small loaf, 1 slice fresh	25g
	toasted	23g
	large loaf 1 medium slice fresh	35g
	toasted	31g
	large loaf, 1 thick slice fresh	45g
	toasted	40g
Wholemeal unsliced bread	small loaf, 1 slice fresh	30g
	toasted	27g
	large loaf 1 medium slice fresh	38g
	toasted	33g
	large loaf, 1 thick slice fresh	55g
	toasted	50g

NB For a thicker end crust of a loaf add on 10g
Crusts are 30% of a slice in weight eg a 30g slice weighs 21g without crust
For fried bread, add on 10g fat per slice

BREAKFAST CEREALS

All-Bran type cereals	eg Branbuds, Grapenuts, All-Bran	
	1 average portion, small	*42g*
	medium	*50g*
	large	*65g*
	1 tablespoon	*7g*
Cornflake type cereals	eg Branflakes, Weetaflakes, Frosties, Crunchy nut Cornflakes, Fruit and Fibre	
	1 average portion, small	*25g*
	medium	*40g*
	large	*55g*
	1 tablespoon	*6g*
	1 variety pack, Cornflakes	*17g*
	Frosties/Crunchy Nut Cornflakes	*23g*
Muesli cereals, not crunchy	eg Alpen, Country Store	
	1 average portion, small	*30g*
	medium	*70g*
	large	*90g*
	1 4oz cup muesli	*100g*
	1 sachet Alpen	*40g*
	1 tablespoon	*15g*
Muesli, crunchy	eg Original Crunchy, Harvest Crunch	
	1 average portion, small	*40g*
	medium	*80g*
	large	*120g*
	1 tablespoon	*20g*
Porridge	made up weight,	
	average portion, small	*150g*
	medium	*200g*
	large	*250g*

Ready Brek	made up weight,	
	average portion, small ($\frac{1}{8}$ pint milk)	*130g*
	medium ($\frac{1}{4}$ pint milk)	*180g*
	large ($\frac{1}{3}$ pint milk)	*225g*

Rice Krispie type cereals	eg Rice Krispies, Ricicles, Puffed Rice	
	Puffa Puffa Rice, Cocopops,	
	Special K, Oat Krunchies	
	1 average portion, small	*20g*
	medium	*30g*
	large	*45g*
	1 tablespoon	*4g*
	1 variety pack, Cocopops	*30g*
	Rice Krispies	*20g*
	Ricicles	*30g*

Shredded Wheat	1	*22g*
	Cubs, average portion	*35g*

Splitz type cereal	average portion, small	*25g*
eg raisin	medium	*40g*
	large	*60g*

Sugar puff type cereals	eg Puffed Wheat, Honey Smacks	
	1 average portion, small	*25g*
	medium	*40g*
	large	*55g*
	1 tablespoon	*6g*

Weetabix	1 bisk	*20g*

CAKES, BUNS AND PASTRIES

Almond slice		*35g*
Angel sandwich	purchased, average slice	*40g*
Apple and mincemeat tart	individual	*88g*
Apple strudel	slice	*115g*
Apple sundae		*53g*
Bakewell tart	individual	*43g*
	slice of large tart	*120g*
Baklava, Greek pastry		*100g*
Banana cake	average slice	*85g*
Battenburg	purchased, average slice	*40g*
Battenburg treat		*39g*
Belgium bun		*110g*
Blackcurrant and apple slice		*32g*
Blackcurrant sundae		*55g*
Black forest gateaux	average portion	*90g*
Chelsea bun		*78g*
Cherry bakewell		*42g*
Cherry fruit cake	average slice	*42g*
Cherry slice		*38g*
Chocolate cake with buttercream	average slice	*65g*
	frozen, average slice	*35g*

Chocolate cupcake		*40g*
Chocolate eclair	purchased, frozen, fresh cream,	*33g*
	bakery or home-made	*90g*
Chocolate fudge slice		*98g*
Chocolate krispie cake		*25g*
Chocolate mini roll		*26g*
Choux bun	filled with cream	*112g*
Coconut cake	average slice	*40g*
Coconut pyramid		*25g*
Country slice		*38g*
Cream horn		*60g*
Cream slice		*100g*
Currant bun		*60g*
Custard tart	individual	*94g*
	slice of large tart	*140g*
Dairy cream sponge	average slice	*39g*
Danish pastry	medium	*110g*
	large	*180g*
Devonshire split		*65g*
Doughnut	apple filling	*85g*
	cream, custard filling	*75g*
	iced	*75g*
	jam filling	*75g*
	large, iced or filled	*130g*
	ring	*60g*

Cakes

Eccles cake		*45g*
Fairy cake		*28g*
Flake cake		*31g*
Flap jack		*60g*
Florentines		*60g*
French fancy	fondant fancy	*30g*
Fruit cake	rich, average slice	*70g*
	rich with marzipan and icing	*70g*
	plain, average slice, homemade	*90g*
Fruit malt loaf		*35g*
Gateaux with fresh cream	average slice	*85g*
Gingerbread man		*50g*
Gingerbread, Parkin		*50g*
Hot cross bun		*50g*
Iced bun		*65g*
Jam tart	individual	*24g*
	slice of large tart	*90g*
Jamaica ginger cake	average slice	*35g*
Lemon meringue pie	average slice	*150g*
Macaroons		*28g*
Madeira	purchased, average slice	*40g*
Meringue	without cream	*8g*
	with cream	*28g*

Melting moment		*30g*
Mini-rolls		*26g*
Mince pie	individual	*48g*
	slice of large pie	*90g*
Paklava, Greek pastry		*100g*
Rock cake		*45g*
Rum Baba		*198g*
Russian cake	sliced, average slice	*180g*
Scones	plain, fruit, cheese	*48g*
	wholemeal	*50g*
	potato	*57g*
	drop scones	*31g*
Sponge cake	no fat, with cream, purchased	*53g*
	with fat and buttercream filling,	
	average slice	*65g*
Sponge finger	1	*4g*
Sultana cake	purchased, average slice	*50g*
Swiss roll	average slice	*30g*
Swiss bun		*50g*
Teacake	fresh	*60g*
	toasted	*55g*
Trifle sponge		*23g*
Vanilla slice		*113g*
Viennese split		*16g*
Welsh cakes		*28g*

Cakes

CHEESE AND CHEESE DISHES

Camembert type cheese	$\frac{1}{8}$ portion	*40g*
Cauliflower cheese	average portion, main dish	*200g*
	side dish	*90g*
Cheddar type cheese	chunk, small	*20g*
	medium	*40g*
	large	*60g*
	grated, 1 tablespoon	*10g*
	matchbox size piece	*30g*
	in ploughmans lunch, average	*120g*
	in sandwich, average (cheese only)	*45g*
Cheese and egg flan	1 slice	*120g*
Cheese and onion pastie		*160g*
Cheese triangle	small	*14g*
	large	*28g*
Cottage cheese	1 small pot	*112g*
	1 tablespoon	*40g*
	in sandwich	*50g*
Cream cheese	in sandwich, average	*30g*
Crispy cheese pancake	purchased frozen, fried	*68g*
Fromage Frais	1 small pot, with or without fruit	*60g*
	1 medium pot, with or without fruit	*100g*
	1 heaped tablespoon	*50g*
Low fat soft cheese, Quark	1 heaped tablespoon	*55g*
Macaroni cheese	average portion	*300g*
	canned, large tin	*430g*
	small tin	*210g*

Pizza	homemade, average portion	_300g_
	frozen, 'mini'	_80g_
	small	_115g_
	medium	_200g_
	large	_454g_
1 average slice, thin base		_140g_
deep pan		_200g_
1 average thin base, cheese and tomato only, serves one		_280g_
1 average deep pan, cheese and tomato only, serves one		_300g_
Average weights of extra toppings, per individual pizza		
	Ham, bacon, pepperoni, salami, sausage	_30g_
	Chicken, tuna	_50g_
	Mushroom, pepper, onion, olives,	_15g_
	Pineapple, sweetcorn	_30g_
	Anchovies	_10g_
Average deep pan pizza, 10″, serves 2		_650g_

Processed cheese	1 slice	_20g_
	1 triangle, small	_14g_
	large	_28g_

| **Vol au vents** | filled with cheese sauce, 1 small | _30g_ |

| **Welsh rarebit** | with toast, 1 slice | _67g_ |
| | topping only | _40g_ |

CONFECTIONERY

Aero milk chocolate,	flat bar	*45g*
Rowntree	chunky bar	*36g*
After eight mints, Rowntree	each	*7g*
American hard gums	tube	*45g*
Aniseed balls	each	*4g*
Applause, Mars	standard bar	*50g*
	funsize bar	*24g*
Banjo bar		*42g*
Barley sugar	piece	*7g*
Barker and Dobson		
menthol BPC	each	*8g*
Barratt's everlasting toffee		
strip		*22g*
Barratt's french nougat	bar	*114g*
Barratt's fruit drops	each	*16g*
Bassett's dolly mixture	per box	*115g*
	per small packet	*56g*
Bassett's jelly babies	per box	*115g*
	per small packet	*56g*
Bassett's liquorice Allsorts	per box	*115g*
	per small packet	*56g*
Bettabar	bar	*30g*
Black Magic, Rowntree	chocolate assortment, each	*8g*
Blackjacks	each	*4g*
Bluebird Woody		
Woodpecker	bar	*17g*
Bon Bons	per packet	*113g*
Boost bars, Cadbury's	Biscuit Boost	*57g*
	Coconut Boost	*53g*
	Peanut Boost	*53g*
Bounty bar	plain or milk chocolate per packet	*58g*
	mini bar	*30g*
Bournville chocolate,		
Cadbury's	small bar	*50g*
Bournville Fruit & Nut Bar,		
Cadbury's		*100g*
Brazil nut chocolates	each	*12g*
Bubble gum	average, each	*4g*
	bubble hamburger	*6g*
	bubblicious	*5g*

Bubble gum, *continued*	high blow	*8g*
	hubba bubba	*6g*
	super bazooka	*8g*
Buttermints	each	*7g*
Butterscotch	per packet	*133g*
Buttons, Cadbury's	chocolate, per standard packet	*33g*
	large packet	*51g*
	4 buttons	*5g*
	creamy white buttons, packet	*32g*

Cadbury's Bar Six		*40g*
Cadbury's Caramel	bar	*50g*
Cadbury's Chomp		*26g*
Cadbury's Creme Egg		*39g*
Cadbury's Crunchie		*42g*
	treat size	*18g*
Cadbury's Curly Wurly		*29g*
Cadbury's Dairy milk		
chocolate	per bar	*50g*
	per square	*7g*
Cadbury's Double Decker	bar	*51g*
	treat size	*19g*
Cadbury's Flake	bar	*34g*
	99er	*9g*
Cadbury's Finger of Fudge	bar	*30g*
	treat size	*15g*
Cadbury's Fruit and Nut		
milk chocolate bar	standard size	*47g*
Cadbury's Golden Crisp		*100g*
Cadbury's Old Jamaica		*100g*
Cadbury's Picnic	bar	*46g*
Cadbury's Royal Mint		*100g*
Cadbury's Spira	per twist	*20g*
Cadbury's Tiffin		*100g*
Cadbury's Turkish		*100g*
Cadbury's Twirl	per finger	*22g*
Cadbury's Walnut and		
Orange	bar	*100g*
Cadbury's Wispa	bar standard	*35g*
	treat size	*14g*
Cadbury's Wholenut	bar	*46g*
Candy stick		*9g*

Candy tots	per packet	*46g*
Caramac bar, Rowntree	per bar	*26g*
	per square	*3g*
Chewetts	per packet	*18g*
	each	*3g*
Chewing gum	average packet	*18g*
	per stick	*2g*
Chews, fruit salad	each	*4g*
Chewy mints	per tube	*39g*
	each	*3g*
Chocolate almond	each	*3g*
Chocolate assortments	each	*10g*
Chocolate brazils	each	*12g*
Chocolate covered ginger	each	*8g*
Chocolate eclairs	per tube	*46g*
	each	*9g*
Chocolate mice	small, each	*3g*
	large, each	*6g*
Chocolate orange/mint crisp	each	*10g*
Chocolate orange bar		*49g*
Chocolate nuts, M & M's	per packet	*47g*
Clear mints	glacier mints, per tube	*39g*
Coconut Grove		*55g*
Coconut ice		*125g*
Cola fizz	(jelly), each	*3g*
Cola sweets	each	*4g*
Cote D'or chocolate	1 square	*8g*
Creamy fudge	1″ square	*11g*

Dairy Crunch, Rowntree	chocolate bar small	*15g*
	large	*35g*
Dextrosol	glucose tablets each	*7g*
Dime bar		*28g*
Dinosaurs egg	each	*19g*
Discos	each	*3g*
Dolly mixtures	per box	*115g*
	per small bag	*56g*
Dracula teeth	each	*4g*
Drifter bar, Rowntree	standard size	*52g*
	mini bar	*17g*

Edinburgh rock	average stick of rock	*100g*
Eggs	creme eggs, each	*39g*
	mini eggs, each	*3g*
	Nutcracker, Terry's per half shell	*18g*
	toffee	*20g*
	Truffle Eggs, Galaxy per half shell	*20g*
Extra strong mints	per tube	*36g*
Everton mints	each	*6g*
Fizzel stick	each	*10g*
Fizzers	per packet	*4g*
Fizzy lizzy	each	*24g*
Flump	(pink marshmallow) each	*2g*
Football chews	each	*4g*
Fruit bon-bons	each	*7g*
Fruit drops	per tube	*16g*
Fruit gums	per tube	*33g*
Fisherman's Friend throat lozenges	each	*1g*
Fruit pastilles	per tube	*40g*
	each	*3g*
Fruit salad chews	each	*4g*
Fruitellas	per tube	*34g*
	each	*4g*
Fry's chocolate cream	bar	*50g*
Fry's turkish delight	bar	*51g*
Fudge	no additions, not finger of fudge, 1 square inch	*11g*
Galaxy	milk chocolate bar	*50g*
Galaxy Gold	bar	*43g*
Ginger, chocolate coated	each	*8g*
Glacier mints	clear mints, per tube	*39g*
	each	*3g*
Gobstoppers	each	*8g*
Golden cup bar, Rowntree		*38g*
Hacks, throat lozengers	each	*3g*
Hall mentholyptus	per packet	*32g*
Hazel whirls	hazelnuts in chocolate, each	*8g*
Hellas mint chocolate		*100g*
Hellas natural filled bars		*100g*
Hollands spearmint arrow		*14g*

Hubba Bubba	per piece	*6g*
Humbugs	each	*8g*
Jelly animal	each	*12g*
Jelly babies	per box	*115g*
	per small bag	*56g*
Jelly beans	each	*8g*
Jelly bears	per packet	*113g*
Jelly boot	each	*12g*
Jelly bottles	each	*2g*
Jelly feet	each	*5g*
Jelly star	each	*4g*
Jelly tots	per packet	*51g*
	each	*1g*
Juicy fruit chewing gum	per packet	*18g*
	per stick	*2g*
Kendal mint cake	each	*52g*
Kinder surprise	each	*20g*
Kit Kat, Rowntree	4 bar	*43g*
	2 bar	*20g*
Kola chew bar		*14g*
Krunch	per bar	*31g*
Lion bar, Rowntree	standard size	*38g*
	mini, cub	*18g*
Liqueur chocolates	each	*8g*
Liquorice allsorts	per box	*115g*
	per small bag	*56g*
Liquorice comfits	each	*1g*
Liquorice imps	each	*8g*
	per packet	*40g*
Liquorice shoelace	each	*6g*
Liquorice sticks	each	*3g*
Liquorice toffees	each	*8g*
Liquorice torpedoes	per packet	*76g*
Liquorice watch	each	*16g*
Lockets throat lozenges	per packet	*50g*
Logger milk chocolate bar, Terry's		*50g*

Logger fruit and nut chocolate bar, Terry's		50g
Lollipops	each	5g
Love hearts	per packet	16g
Lucozade tablets	each	4g

M & M's, Mars	chocolate	52g
	peanut	52g
Macaroon bar		45g
Mac throat lozenges	each	3g
Maltesers	per packet	40g
	each	2g
Mars bar	kingsize	100g
	regular	68g
	mini	20g
Marshmallows	each	5g
Marshmallow bars chocolate coated	per bar	11g
Marzipan bars chocolate coated	per bar	41g
Marzipan fruits	each	12g
Matchmakers	each	2g
Milady orange drop	each	7g
Milk chew	each	4g
Milk gums	each	2g
Milk chocolate assortment	each	10g
Milk chocolate bar	average	35g
	1 square	7g
Milk chocolate orange bar	standard size	49g
Milk chocolate raisins	per packet	44g
	each	2g
Milky bar, Nestle	small	13g
	medium	20g
	large	35g
	chunky	20g
	1 square	3g
Milky Way, Mars	standard size	55g
	mini bar	17g
Minstrels, Galaxy	per packet	50g
	family packet	180g
	each	3g

Mint caramel chews	each	*8g*
Mint imperials	each	*2g*
Mintips	per packet	*33g*
Mintolas, Rowntree	per small packet	*60g*
	per large packet	*113g*
	each	*5g*
Mintoes	per packet	*100g*
	each	*5g*
Mints	extra strong, per tube	*36g*
	each	*2g*
Monster fizz sherbet	per packet	*8g*
Murray fruits, Murray mints	per tube	*50g*
	each	*5g*
Munchies, Rowntree	per packet	*44g*
	each	*4g*

Neapolitans	Terry's naps. each	*8g*
Nestle collection bars		*100g*
Newberry fruits	each	*9g*
Noisette cup	each	*8g*
Nougat	per large bar	*114g*
	per small bar	*70g*
	per sweet	*10g*
Novo	bar	*50g*
Nudge	bar	*35g*
Nutty chew	bar	*14g*
Nutty bar		*56g*

Opal fruits	per packet	*114g*
	per tube	*56g*
	each	*5g*
Orange and lemon slices	each	*5g*
Orange milk chocolate	Terry's milk chocolate orange, bar	*49g*
Orange pips	per packet	*38g*
Orange plain chocolate	Terry's plain chocolate orange, bar	*49g*
Orbit gum	per stick	*2g*
Ovaltine	bar	*50g*

Pacers	per tube	*54g*
	each	*5g*
Parma violets	per packet	*16g*
	each	*1g*
Pastilles	(fruit pastilles) per tube	*40g*
	each	*3g*
	(throat pastilles) each	*2g*
Peanut brittle	per bar	*58g*
Pear drops	large, each	*6g*
	small, each	*2g*
Penny chew	each	*4g*
Peppermint creams	not chocolate covered	*6g*
	chocolate covered	*7g*
Peppermint lump	each	*9g*
Pineapple chunks	each	*5g*
Polo fruits, Rowntree	per tube	*30g*
Polo mints, Rowntree	per tube	*22g*
	each	*2g*
Pontefract cakes	each	*4g*
Pyramint		*30g*

Quality Street	chocolate assortment, each	*8g*

Rainbow drops	per packet	*18g*
Refreshers	per tube	*14g*
	each	*1g*
Revels, Mars	per packet	*40g*
	per family packet	*105g*
	each	*2g*
Ripple bar, Galaxy		*32g*
Ritter chocolate bars	all types	*100g*
Rolos, Rowntree	large tube	*63g*
	small	*43g*
	each	*7g*
Rock	1 average stick	*100g*
Rum and raisin toffee	each	*8g*
Rum and raisin fudge	1 square inch	*11g*

Confectionery

Sarotti chocolate bars	all types	100g
Sesame snaps	per packet	30g
Sherbet bon bons	each	7g
Sherbet pips	each	1g
Shout bar		46g
Smarties, Rowntree	per tube	36g
	per box	125g
	each	1g
Snickers bar, Mars	standard	48g
	mini bar	20g
Soft mints	per tube	45g
Stampede	per bar	32g
Strepsils throat lozenges	each	3g
Suchard chocolate bars	all types	100g
Suchard praline milk chocolate bar		42g
Suchard Toblerone	small	50g
	medium	100g
	large	200g
Sugared almonds	each	6g
Sweet cigarette	each	7g

Terry's Bitz	per bar	50g
Terry's Crispy Caramel		45g
Terry's Logger	per bar	50g
Terry's milk chocolate orange bar		49g
Terry's neapolitans, 'naps'	each	8g
Terry's plain chocolate bar	small	50g
	medium	100g
	large	150g
Terry's plain chocolate bar with marzipan		41g
Terry's Waifa bar	plain or milk chocolate	35g
Tic-Tacs	per packet	12g
Tiger tots	per packet	51g
Toblerone	small	50g
	medium	100g
	large	200g
Toffee Cup		23g

Toffee Crisp bar		*40g*
Toffees	not chocolate-covered, no additions,	
	each	*8g*
Toffee egg		*20g*
Toffos	per tube	*50g*
Toffets	per box	*48g*
	each	*2g*
Topic	bar	*54g*
Tools, chocolate	each	*11g*
Tooty Frooties, Tooty		
Minties	per packet	*51g*
Tracker	bar	*40g*
Trebor chew bars	each	*8g*
Trebor fruit chew	each	*4g*
Trebor mints	per packet	*28g*
Trebor phantom chew	each	*10g*
Tunes throat lozenges	per packet	*37g*
	each	*3g*
Twix, Mars	bar	*50g*
Turkish delight, Frys	chocolate covered bar	*51g*
	per square	*15g*
Vollmilch bar		*100g*
Victory V's	per packet	*50g*
Walnut Whip, Rowntree	each	*37g*
Wham bar		*43g*
Wine gums	each	*3g*
Wrigley's chewing gum	per stick	*2g*
Yes	per packet	*37g*
Yoghurt coated peanuts		
and raisins	each	*1g*
Yogi bar		*39g*
Yorkie chocolate bar		*70g*
Yorkie peanut, raisin and		
biscuit, honey and		
almond		*70g*

Confectionery

EGG AND EGG DISHES

1 duck's egg	boiled, no shell, average size	*75g*
1 hen's egg	boiled, no shell, average size	*50g*
	no shell, size 1	*67g*
	no shell, size 2	*61g*
	no shell, size 3	*57g*
	no shell, size 4	*47g*
Egg custard	average portion	*140g*
Fried egg	average	*60g*
Egg fried rice	average portion	*270g*
Poached egg	average size	*50g*
Egg mayonnaise	average portion	*120g*
Egg, white	average size	*32g*
Egg yolk	average size	*18g*
Omelette	2 eggs	*120g*
Quiche	average slice, small	*70g*
	medium	*120g*
	large	*190g*
Scotch egg	average size	*120g*
	mini, picnic egg	*60g*
Scrambled egg	2 eggs	*120g*
	Mcdonalds	*94g*
Souffle	average portion	*110g*

FATS

Butter or hard margarine	average spread on slice bread, thin		*7g*
		medium	*10g*
		thick	*12g*
	average spread on roll, thin		*10g*
		medium	*12g*
		thick	*15g*
	average spread on toasted crumpet		*15g*
	1 curl		*8g*
	1 portion, packed		*10g*
	1 restaurant portion, not packed		*20g*
	1 teaspoon		*5g*
Butter in 'boil in the bag'			*15g*
Butter/margarine in baked potato			*20g*
Flora	1 portion pack		*10g*
Soft margarine, low fat spread,	average spread on slice bread, thin		*5g*
		medium	*7g*
		thick	*10g*
	average spread on roll, thin		*7g*
		medium	*10g*
		thick	*12g*
	average spread on toasted crumpet		*10g*
	thin scraping on crispbread		*2g*
	1 teaspoon		*5g*
Oil	1 tablespoon		*11g*
	1 teaspoon		*3g*

NB For toast add on 2g spread per slice

FISH AND FISH PRODUCTS

Anchovy	1 anchovy	*3g*
	1 small tin	*50g*
	average on pizza	*10g*

Cockle	1 cockle	*4g*
	1 small jar	*142g*
	average portion	*25g*

Cod	1 average fillet, small	*50g*
	medium	*120g*
	large	*175g*
	1 average steak	*50g*
	in batter, small	*120g*
	medium	*180g*
	large	*225g*
	in batter/crumb, oven crispy	*100g*
	in sauce, purchased, frozen	*170g*

| Cod roe | average portion fried/grilled | *116g* |
| | in batter, average portion | *160g* |

Crab	1 tablespoon crab meat	*40g*
	1 small can	*85g*
	1 large can	*170g*

| Crabstick | 1 stick | *17g* |

| Dogfish | see rock salmon | |

| Dover sole | 1 whole, average, with bone | *250g* |

| Eel | 1 slice, 5″ long | *20g* |

| Filet-o-fish | Mcdonalds | *130g* |

| Fish cakes | 1 frozen, fried/grilled | *50g* |
| | 1 fried in batter | *100g* |

| Fish in a bun | fried fish in a bun, fish only | *75g* |

Fish in batter	fish and chip shop, average	*190g*
	fast food outlet, average	*160g*
Fish in sauce	frozen, purchased	*170g*
Fish fingers	1 fish finger, fried/grilled	*28g*
	1 jumbo size fish finger	*60g*
Fish paste	1 small jar	*35g*
	1 medium jar	*53g*
	1 large jar	*75g*
	average spread on slice of bread	*10g*
Fish paté	average portion, as starter	*40g*
Fish pie	(fish and potato, not pastry)	
	average serving	*250g*
	frozen purchased	*227g*
Herring	1 filleted, small	*85g*
	medium	*119g*
	filleted in tomato sauce, 1 can	*200g*
	pickled, 1 roll mop herring	*90g*
Herring roe	average portion fried/grilled	*85g*
Haddock	1 fillet small	*50g*
	medium	*85g*
	large	*120g*
	1 average fillet fried in batter, small	*120g*
	medium	*170g*
	large	*220g*
	1 average fillet, purchased	
	breadcrumbed, fried/grilled	*120g*
	1 average fillet, oven baked	*100g*
Kedgeree	average portion	*300g*
King prawn	1, no shell	*8g*

Kipper	1 grilled fillet, small	*85g*
	medium	*125g*
	large	*170g*
	1 'Boil-in-the-bag', with	
	butter	*170g*
	1 can kipper fillets	*200g*
Lemon sole	1 average, grilled/fried/steamed, with	
	bone, small	*90g*
	medium	*150g*
	large	*220g*
Lobster	average portion, 2 tablespoons	*85g*
	half dressed lobster, with shell	*250g*
Mackerel	1 average smoked mackerel, small	*100g*
	medium	*150g*
	large	*200g*
	1 whole fried mackerel	*220g*
	1 can mackerel in oil,	
	small can	*200g*
	large can	*425g*
	1 can mackerel in curry/tomato/mustard	
	sauce	*125g*
Mussels	1 mussel, no shell	*7g*
	1 average portion, no shells	*40g*
	1 jar mussels small	*80g*
	large	*198g*
	1 small tin smoked mussels	*105g*
Oysters	1 oyster with shell	*42g*
	1 oyster without shell	*10g*
	1 dozen oysters, edible portion	*120g*
	1 can smoked oysters	*105g*
Paella	frozen, purchased	*284g*
Pilchards	1 canned pilchard in tomato sauce	*55g*
	1 can pilchards, small	*215g*
	large	*425g*

Plaice	1 average fillet plaice, steamed/grilled,	
	small	*75g*
	medium	*130g*
	large	*180g*
	1 average fillet plaice, in breadcrumbs,	
	fried, small	*90g*
	medium	*150g*
	large	*200g*
	1 average fillet plaice, in batter, fried,	
	small	*150g*
	medium	*200g*
	large	*250g*
	1 average whole plaice in batter/	
	crumb, oven ready	*112g*
	1 average whole stuffed plaice,	
	purchased frozen	*190g*
Prawns	1 prawn, without shell	*3g*
	1 average portion prawns, shelled	*60g*
	1 king prawn, without shell	*8g*
	half a pint of prawns, shelled	*142g*
	portion of prawns in prawn cocktail	*40g*
	1 small jar prawns	*100g*
Rock salmon (dogfish)	1 average portion in batter, fried,	
	small	*150g*
	medium	*200g*
	large	*250g*
Roe	1 average portion cods roe,	
	grilled/fried	*116g*
	1 average portion cods roe in batter	*160g*
	1 average portion herring roe,	
	fried/grilled	*85g*
Salmon	1 average salmon steak,	
	steamed/poached	*100g*
	1 average portion smoked salmon	*56g*
	1 average portion canned salmon	*100g*
	1 average portion canned salmon in a	
	sandwich	*45g*

Sardines	1 canned sardine	*25g*
	1 average portion canned sardines	*100g*
	1 average portion in sandwich	*50g*
Scampi	1 piece scampi, crumb coated	*15g*
	1 average portion of scampi, fried in breadcrumbs	*150g*
Shrimps	potted, average portion	*50g*
Skate	1 average portion skate, fried in batter	*200g*
	1 average portion skate, cooked in butter	*150g*
Sprats	1 sprat fried/grilled with bones	*55g*
	1 portion sprats, fried/grilled with bones	*220g*
Squid	1 average portion cooked squid	*65g*
	1 average ring of squid, fried in batter (kalamares)	*20g*
	1 average portion fried squid in batter	*120g*
Trout	1 average trout, fried/grilled, with bones	*180g*
	without bones	*120g*
	1 average stuffed trout	*220g*
Taramasalata	average portion, 1 tablespoon	*45g*
	1 average tub, purchased	*112g*
Tuna	1 average portion for sandwich filling	*45g*
	1 average portion with salad	*92g*
	1 small can	*100g*
White fish	(If type not specified)	
	small fillet	*100g*
	medium fillet	*150g*
	large fillet	*180g*
Whelks	1 whelk, without shell	*7g*
	1 average portion whelks	*30g*

Whitebait	1 whitebait, fried in flour	*4g*
	1 average portion, fried	*80g*

Whiting	1 average portion, fried in batter,		
		small	*120g*
		medium	*180g*
		large	*240g*
	1 average portion, steamed		*85g*

FRUIT

Apple	1 raw small eating (6 to lb) with core	*75g*
	without core	*67g*
	1 raw medium eating (4 to lb)	*112g*
	without core	*100g*
	1 raw large eating (2–3 to lb)	*170g*
	without core	*153g*
	stewed with sugar, average portion	*140g*
	1 baked, average portion	*190g*
Apricot	1 raw without stone	*65g*
	canned with syrup/juice, average portion	*140g*
	1 dried	*8g*
Avocado pear	1 raw small without skin or stone	*100g*
	1 raw medium without skin or stone	*145g*
	1 raw large without skin or stone	*195g*
	average 1/2 pear	*75g*
Banana	1 raw small without skin	*80g*
	1 raw medium without skin	*100g*
	1 raw large without skin	*120g*
	1 raw slice without skin	*5g*
	10 dried chips	*13g*
Bilberries	1 raw	*2g*
Blackberries	1 raw	*5g*
	stewed with sugar, average portion	*140g*
Blackcurrants	5 raw	*2g*
	Stewed with sugar, average portion	*140g*
Cherries	1 raw eating without stone	*10g*
Clementines	1 raw small without skin	*40g*
	1 raw medium without skin	*60g*
	1 raw large without skin	*80g*

Currants	4 dried	*1g*
	1 heaped tablespoon, dried	*25g*
Damson	1 raw without stone	*15g*
Date	1 raw without stone	*25g*
	1 dried without stone	*15g*
Fig	1 raw	*55g*
	1 dried	*20g*
Fruit juices	see beverages	
Fruit salad	canned with syrup/juice average portion	*105g*
	fresh with syrup/juice, average portion	*140g*
Gooseberries	stewed with sugar, average portion	*140g*
Grapes	1 raw	*5g*
	1 seedless	*2g*
	small bunch	*100g*
Grapefruit	1 raw small with skin	*250g*
	1 raw medium with skin	*340g*
	1 raw large with skin	*425g*
	1/2, raw flesh only	*80g*
	canned with syrup/juice, average portion	*105g*
Greengage	1 raw without stone	*50g*
Kiwi fruit	1 raw medium without skin	*60g*
Kumquat	1 raw medium	*8g*
Lemon	juice from 1/2 lemon	*10g*
	1 slice for drinks	*20g*
Loquat	1 raw without stone	*40g*

| Lychee | 1 raw without stone or skin | *15g* |
| | canned without stone | *13g* |

Mandarin orange	no skin, small	*60g*
	medium	*100g*
	large	*140g*

Mango	1 quarter, without stone or peel	*160g*
	1 slice	*40g*
	canned in syrup average portion	*105g*

| Medlar | 1 raw, without stone | *60g* |

Melon	canteloupe, 1 slice without skin	*150g*
	honeydew, 1 slice without skin	*180g*
	watermelon, 1 slice without skin	*200g*

| Mineola | average with skin | *200g* |

| Mixed dried fruit | 1 heaped tablespoon | *25g* |

Nectarine	1 raw, small without skin	*130g*
	1 raw medium without skin	*150g*
	1 raw large without skin	*190g*

| Olive | without stone, stuffed olive | *3g* |

Orange	1 raw small without skin	*120g*
	1 raw medium without skin	*160g*
	1 raw large without skin	*210g*
	juice from 1 orange	*55g*

| Passion fruit | 1 average, flesh and seeds only | *15g* |

| Paw paw (papaya) | 1 average slice, without skin or stone | *140g* |

Peach	1 raw small without stone	*70g*
	1 raw medium without stone	*110g*
	1 raw large without stone	*150g*
	canned with syrup/juice, average portion	*105g*

Fruit

Fruit

Pear	conference, 1 raw medium	*170g*
	comice, 1 raw medium	*250g*
	canned, ½ pear	*60g*
Pineapple	1 raw large slice without skin	*80g*
	canned, one ring, or 6 chunks	*40g*
	1 fritter	*60g*
Plum	raw, small without stone	*30g*
	medium without stone	*55g*
	large without stone	*85g*
Prunes	1, dried	*10g*
	6 stewed, without stones	*24g*
Raisins	1, tablespoon dried	*30g*
Raspberries	1, raw	*4g*
	raw, average portion, (15 raspberries)	*60g*
	canned with syrup/juice, average portion	*90g*
Rhubarb	stewed, with sugar, average portion	*140g*
Satsuma	see tangerine	
Sharon fruit	1 raw	*110g*
Strawberry	1 raw	*12g*
	canned with syrup, average portion	*90g*
Sultanas	1 tablespoon, dried	*30g*
Tangerine	1 raw small without skin	*50g*
	1 raw medium without skin	*70g*
	1 raw large without skin	*90g*

MEAT AND MEAT PRODUCTS

Bacon	1 rasher back bacon, fried/grilled	
	average	*25g*
	1 rasher middle bacon, fried/grilled	
	average	*40g*
	1 rasher streaky bacon, fried/grilled	
	average	*20g*
	1 portion bacon average	*45g*
	1 gammon steak average	*170g*
	in a bun, average	*100g*
	with egg in a bun, average	*120g*
	Mcdonalds, bacon and egg Mcmuffin	*140g*
	Wimpy bacon in a bun	*105g*
	Wimpy bacon and egg in a bun	*170g*

Beefburgers	no bun, 100% beef, 56g raw, fried/	
	grilled	*34g*
	80% beef, 56g raw, fried/	
	grilled	*36g*
	economy, 60% beef, 56g raw, fried/	
	grilled	*40g*
	100% beef, quarterpounder,	
	fried/grilled	*78g*
	80% beef, quarterpounder,	
	fried/grilled	*90g*
	in a bun, average	*105g*
	with cheese, cheeseburger,	
	average	*115g*
	quarterpounder, average	*180g*
	quarter pounder with cheese,	
	average	*200g*
	Mcdonalds, hamburger	*103g*
	cheeseburger	*117g*
	quarterpounder	*160g*
	quarterpounder	
	with cheese	*186g*
	Big-Mac	*207g*
	Wimpy hamburger	*106g*
	cheeseburger	*120g*
	quarterpounder	*205g*

Beefburgers, *continued*	quarterpounder with cheese	219g
	halfpounder	307g
	kingsize	200g
	in batter, average	130g
Beef casserole or curry	average portion, small	250g
	medium	330g
	large	450g
Beef and onion pastie		160g
Canned steak/steak and kidney pie	small	213g
	large	425g
Cornish pastie	medium	155g
	large	260g
Scotch pie		112g
Steak pie, large	small slice	90g
	medium slice	120g
	large slice	150g
Steak pie	individual	200g
Steak and kidney pie	individual	200g
Steak and potato pie	individual	200g
Steak and kidney pudding	individual	160g
	small	230g
	large	450g
Beef, minced	stewed, small, average portion	150g
	medium, average portion	200g
	large, average portion	350g
	stewed with gravy and vegetables, average portion	330g
	stewed canned, small	200g
	large	392g

Beef, roast	small, average portion	*90g*
	medium, average portion	*120g*
	large, average portion	*180g*
	1 slice roast beef, thinly sliced	*30g*
	1 slice roast beef, thickly sliced	*45g*
	1 portion in gravy, purchased frozen,	
	beef	*59g*
	gravy	*55g*
Beef, steaks	1 fillet steak, 5oz, fried/grilled	*115g*
	8oz, fried/grilled	*180g*
	1 minute steak, fried/grilled	*80g*
	1 rump steak, 5oz, fried/grilled	*115g*
	8oz, fried/grilled	*180g*
	1 T-bone steak, 8oz, fried/grilled	*180g*
	12oz, fried/grilled	*270g*
Stewed beef	small average portion	*150g*
	medium average portion	*200g*
	large average portion	*350g*
Stewed beef and vegetables	in gravy, average portion	*330g*
Black pudding	1 slice	*30g*
	1 portion	*75g*
Bolognese sauce	average portion	*220g*
Braising steak	see Stewed beef	
Burgerbites in baked beans	small tin, beans	*170g*
	burgerbites	*55g*
Cannelloni	average portion	*450g*
	frozen ready meal, serves one	*250g*
Chickbits	in baked beans, small tin, beans	*170g*
	chickbits	*55g*
Chicken in a bun	fried chicken sandwich, chicken only	*70g*
	with bun	*130g*

Meat

Chicken breast steak	in breadcrumbs, fried	*100g*
Chicken casserole or curry	small average portion	*250g*
	medium average portion	*330g*
	large average portion	*450g*
Chicken cordon bleu	fried or grilled	*160g*
Chicken fingers	fried, each	*15g*
Chicken Kiev	fried or grilled	*160g*
Chicken nuggets	pieces, baked/fried, each	*16g*
	6 nuggets average portion	*100g*
	Mcdonalds, 6, 9, 20 nuggets	*109g/ 164g/ 353g*
Chicken pie	individual	*190g*
	large	*480g*
	1 slice of large pie, small	*90g*
	medium	*120g*
	large	*150g*
	individual, with mushroom/vegetables	*190g*
Chicken portions	1 breast, no bone, small	*100g*
	medium	*130g*
	large	*150g*
	1 drumstick, with bone	*90g*
	edible portion	*47g*
	1 leg, with bone	*165g*
	edible portion	*90g*
	1 thigh, with bone	*75g*
	edible portion	*45g*
	1 wing, with bone	*55g*
	edible portion	*25g*
	1 quarter, edible portion	*190g*
	1 half, edible portion	*350g*
Chicken, roast	small average portion	*90g*
	medium average portion	*140g*
	large average portion	*180g*

Chicken roast, *continued*	in gravy, purchased frozen, chicken	*59g*
	gravy	*55g*
	1 slice roast, breast	*40g*
Chicken roll	1 slice	*19g*
Chicken tikka and tandoori chicken	see Indian dishes	
Chilli con carne	no rice	*220g*
Chinese dishes	beef dishes, eg beef in oyster sauce	*360g*
	char-sui buns, steamed, small	*60g*
	large	*112g*
	chicken dishes eg chicken with	
	mushrooms	*400g*
	chop suey dishes eg chicken chop suey	*450g*
	chow mein dishes eg beef chow mein	*350g*
	pancake roll, small	*90g*
	large	*140g*
	spare ribs in sauce	*340g*
	sweet and sour dishes eg sweet and	
	sour pork	*300g*
	pork balls only	*150g*
Chopped ham and pork	average slice	*14g*
Corned beef	1 slice, thin	*30g*
	thick	*50g*
	1 small can	*198g*
Cornish pastie	medium	*155g*
	large	*260g*
Cottage pie/Shepherds pie	average portion	*300g*
Curries	average eg Bhuna, Dhansak, Dupiaza,	
	Kashmir, Korma, Madras,	
	Malaya, Patia, Rogan Josh,	
	Vindaloo	*350g*
	(See also Indian dishes)	

Meat

49

Duck	breast and wing, roast, meat and skin only	*185g*
Faggots	in gravy, 2	*150g*
Fillet steak	average, 5oz, fried/grilled	*115g*
Game	1 grouse, with bone	*350g*
	meat only	*160g*
	1 partridge, with bone	*550g*
	meat only	*260g*
	1 pheasant, with bone	*800g*
	meat only	*430g*
	1 pigeon, with bone	*240g*
	meat only	*115g*
	1 rabbit, with bone	*850g*
	meat only	*510g*
	venison, average portion	*120g*
Game pie	average slice	*175g*
Ham	average slice	*23g*
	honey glazed ham, average slice	*28g*
	canned ham, average slice, thin	*35g*
	thick	*45g*
	very thinly sliced ham, 1 slice	*11g*
Hamburgers	see beefburgers	
Haslet	average slice	*14g*
Heart	1 cooked whole lambs	*200g*
Indian dishes	biriani, rice and meat	*400g*
	biriani sauce	*200g*
	chicken tikka, as starter	*120g*
	chicken tikka, as main course	*200g*
	chicken tikka mossala	*300g*
	curry eg. Bhuna, Dhansak, Dupiaza, Kashmir, Korma, Madras, Malaya, Patia, Rogan Josh, Vindaloo	*350g*

Indian dishes, *continued*	kebab, rashmi, seesh, shami, as starter	*140g*
	meat tikka, main course	*200g*
	samosa, meat, small	*40g*
	medium	*70g*
	large	*120g*
	tandoori chicken, as starter	*100g*
	tandoori chicken, main course,	
	half chicken	*700g*
	edible portion	*350g*
	whole chicken	*1400g*
	edible portion	*700g*

Irish stew	average portion	*330g*
	canned, 1 large can	*425g*

Kebab	average portion meat on skewer	*90g*
	doner kebab, small, meat	*85g*
	pitta bread	*75g*
	salad	*70g*
	doner kebab, large, meat	*130g*
	pitta bread	*95g*
	salad	*90g*
	kofte kebab, meat only	*90g*
	rashmi, seesh, shami kebab,	
	Indian starter	*140g*
	shish kebab, meat on skewer,	
	meat only	*85g*

Kidney	in gravy, average portion	*112g*
	in individual steak and kidney pie	*15g*
	1 tablespoon cooked kidney	*40g*
	1 whole lambs kidney	*90g*
	1 whole pigs kidney	*140g*

Lamb casserole or curry	small average portion	*250g*
	medium average portion	*330g*
	large average portion	*450g*

Lamb chop	average chump chop, with bone,	
	fried/grilled	*160g*
	edible portion only	*90g*
	average cutlet, with bone,	
	fried or grilled	*98g*
	edible portion only	*50g*
	average braising chop, with bone	*150g*
	edible portion only	*85g*
Lamb, roast	small average portion	*90g*
	medium average portion	*120g*
	large average portion	*180g*
	average slice	*30g*
Lasagne	average portion	*450g*
	purchased frozen ready meal for one	*250g*
Liver	1 slice lambs/calves, fried/grilled	*40g*
	1 slice pigs/ox, fried/grilled	*50g*
	1 portion, in gravy, liver only	*70g*
	1 portion, with onions in gravy,	
	purchased frozen	*142g*
Luncheon meat	average slice	*14g*
	thick slice	*20g*
Meat dishes	average portions	
	Cannelloni	*450g*
	Chilli con carne, no rice	*220g*
	Hot-pots	*330g*
	Irish stew	*330g*
	Lasagne	*450g*
	Meatballs, 6 meat balls, canned	*80g*
	Moussaka	*330g*
	Shepherds pie, Cottage pie	*300g*
	Spaghetti bolognese, sauce only	*220g*
	Stews, Casseroles, average	*330g*
	Tacos, 1 filled shell, meat only	*65g*
	taco shell	*14g*

Minute steak	average fried/grilled	*80g*
Partridge	see game	
Pastie	see cornish pastie, beef pies	
Pate	average portion as starter	*120g*
	average on slice of bread	*40g*
Pheasant	see game	
Pies	see beef pies, chicken pies, pork pies sausage rolls	
Pigeon	see game	
Pork casserole or curry	average portion, small	*250g*
	medium	*330g*
	large	*450g*
Pork chops	chump chops, no bone, fried/grilled	*230g*
	lean pork escallope, fried/grilled	*75g*
	loin steaks, no bone, fried/grilled	*120g*
	rib end chops, with bone, fried/grilled	*165g*
	edible portion	*85g*
	shoulder steak, no bone, fried/grilled	*135g*
	spare rib chops, with bone, fried/grilled	*220g*
	edible portion	*140g*
	streaky slices, with bone, fried/grilled	*170g*
	edible portion	*110g*
	other pork chops, average, with bone, fried/grilled	*150g*
	edible portion	*75g*
Pork pies	Buffet pie	*75g*
	Individual pie	*140g*
	Large/family pie	*450g*
	Mini pie	*50g*
	Slice pie	*60g*
	Veal and ham pie, 1 slice	*140g*

Meat

Pork, roast	small average portion	_90g_
	medium average portion	_120g_
	large average portion	_180g_
	average slice	_40g_

| **Rabbit** | see game | |

| **Rump steak** | average, 5oz, fried/grilled | _115g_ |

| **Salami** | 1 average slice | _17g_ |

Sausages	1 pork/beef, large fried/grilled	_60g_
	1 pork/beef, thin, fried/grilled	_35g_
	1 pork/beef, buffet, fried/grilled	_12g_
	1 chipolata	_24g_
	1 hot dog sausage/frankfurter, small	_23g_
	large	_47g_
	1 German sausage, bratwurst	_75g_
	1 cabanos sausage, whole	_125g_
	1 saveloy	_65g_
	1 peperami	_25g_
	Mcdonalds sausage pattie	_45g_
	sausage and egg	_180g_
	Sausage in batter	_115g_

Sausage rolls	1 sausage roll, small	_35g_
	medium	_60g_
	large	_85g_
	1 'mini' sausage roll	_21g_

| **Scotch pie** | individual | _112g_ |

| **Shepherds pie** | cottage pie, average portion | _300g_ |

| **Spam** | 1 average slice | _14g_ |
| | fritter | _30g_ |

| **Spare rib chops** | with bone, fried/grilled | _220g_ |
| | edible portion | _140g_ |

Spare ribs	1 rack, 4 ribs, with bone	*120g*
	edible portion	*60g*
	average portion, no bone	*120g*
	chinese spare ribs in sauce	*340g*
	Kentucky, spare ribs with bone	*224g*
	spare ribs in full house, with bone	*112g*
	1 Ungers King Rib	*60g*
Steak	see beef	
Steak and kidney pies,	see beef pies	
Stewing steak	see beef stewed	
T-bone steak	average, 8oz, fried/grilled	*180g*
Tandoori chicken	see Indian dishes	
Tongue	1 average slice	*25g*
Tripe	1 average portion, stewed	*150g*
Turkey	1 average steak	*100g*
Turkey burger	1 breaded and fried	*90g*
Turkey roll	1 slice	*19g*
Roast turkey	as roast chicken	
Veal, cutlet/escallope	in breadcrumbs, fried	*150g*
Veal and ham pie	1 slice	*140g*
Venison	1 average portion	*120g*

Meat

MILK, CREAM, ICE-CREAM AND YOGHURT

Milk and cream

Milk		
	1 pint	*585g*
	½ pint	*293g*
	⅓ pint	*195g*
	¼ pint	*146g*
	⅛ pint	*73g*
	1 tablespoon	*20g*
	1 dessertspoon	*15g*
	1 teaspoon	*5g*
	whole, in 1 cup tea/coffee	*25g*
	in 1 mug tea/coffee	*30g*
	semi-skim, in 1 cup tea/coffee	*30g*
	in 1 mug tea/coffee	*40g*
	skimmed, in 1 cup tea/coffee	*35g*
	in 1 mug tea/coffee	*50g*
	average glass	*200g*
	with cereals average portion	*100g*
	canned, semi-skimmed, ready to drink	*300g*
	evaporated, 1 small can	*170g*
	individual portion pack for tea	*15g*
Coffeemate	1 teaspoon	*3g*
Dried milk	1 teaspoon	*3g*
Cream	1 small carton(5 fl. oz)	*150g*
	1 large carton(10 fl. oz)	*300g*
	1 tablespoon, single	*20g*
	1 tablespoon, double	*30g*
	1 tablespoon, aerosol cream	*10g*
	individual portion pack for coffee	*15g*
	whipped on fruit or cake	*45g*
Dream Topping	on fruit or cake	*15g*
Flavoured milk	crazy milk, individual carton	*214g*
	bottle (500mls)	*544g*
Mars bar milk	(200 mls)	*227g*

Milkshake, thick with ice-cream	Mcdonalds, Wimpy etc.	*300g*
Yoghurt drinks	individual bottles/cartons (200 mls)	*210g*
	large bottles, cartons (500 mls)	*525g*

Ice creams and lollies

Ace, Lyons Maid		*81g*
Apple Maid, Lyons Maid		*53g*
Big Squeeze, Lyons Maid		*74g*
Bombe	chocolate covered, individual	*60g*
Bonanza, Walls		*61g*
Bounty, Mars		*50g*
Calippo, Walls		*114g*
Catering brickette	Lyons maid, strawberry	*31g*
	vanilla	*31g*
	Walls, strawberry, vanilla	*36g*
Choc ice	chunky, (Walls)	*50g*
	classico, (Lyons Maid)	*44g*
	dark and golden, (Walls)	*46g*
	dark satin, (Lyons Maid)	*42g*
	dream, (Walls)	*56g*
	figaro (Lyons Maid)	
	small	*51g*
	large	*80g*
	fruit and nut dream, (Walls)	*66g*
	golden vanilla, (Walls)	*46g*
	nutcracker, (Lyons Maid)	*57g*
	silky smooth, (Lyons Maid)	*42g*
Choc 'n' Nut Crunch, Lyons Maid		*59g*
Cornetto, Walls	choc 'n' cherry, supercone	*94g*
	choc and nut	*74g*
	mint choc chip	*75g*
	strawberry	*81g*
Cornish Strawberry Mivvi, Lyons Maid		*63g*
Fab, Lyons Maid		*61g*
Feast, Walls	chocolate, coconut, mint	*76g*

Florida Orange Mini Juice, Walls		36g
Freaky Foot, Walls		50g
Fresto, Walls	lemon, strawberry	81g
Funny faces, Walls		44g

Hostess Cup, Lyons Maid	chocolate, strawberry	75g

Ice cream	bar, golden vanilla, Walls	49g
	block, 1 average slice	75g
	1 average scoop	60g
	Mr Whippy style, 1 cornet, ice-cream	110g
	cornet	5g
	tub	60g
	individual slices, vanilla	36g

King cone, Lyons Maid	chocolate mint, vanilla	66g
	cornish dairy	76g
	dairy strawberry	73g
	royale	95g

Lemonbrulée, Walls		111g

Magnifico, Walls		117g
Mars Bar, Mars		60g
Magnum, Walls		94g
Merlin Brew, Lyons Maid		47g
Mini Milk, Walls	strawberry, vanilla, chocolate	30g
Mint crisp, Lyons Maid		70g
Mr Men, Lyons Maid	all types except dairy	45g
	dairy	40g

Nobbly Bobbly, Lyons Maid		67g

Orange Delight, Lyons Maid		58g
Orange Fruitie, Walls		77g
Orange Maid, Lyons Maid		71g

Pineapple Mivvi, Lyons Maid		63g
Pzazz, Walls		74g

Raspberry Mivvi, Lyons Maid		*47g*
Raspberry and cream Mivvi,		
Lyons Maid		*65g*
Ready Edie, Lyons Maid		*50g*
Red Alert, Walls		*58g*
Romanza, Walls	1 average slice	*59g*

Sky, Walls		*59g*
Snickers, Mars		*60g*
Sparkles, Walls	lemonade, orangeade, strawberry	*57g*
Spin, Walls		*75g*
Stick Up, Walls		*35g*
Strawberry Split, Walls		*67g*
Sundae Cups, Lyons Maid	chocolate	*60g*
	cornish	*70g*
	raspberry	*67g*
	vanilla	*46g*
Super sprint, Lyons Maid		*63g*

Tangle Twister, Walls		*80g*
Tempo, Walls		*55g*
Toffee Crumble, Lyons Maid		*56g*
Triple Choc, Lyons Maid		*61g*
Tropical Juice bar, Lyons		
Maid		*61g*
Tub, ice cream		*60g*
Turkish Delight, Lyons Maid		*67g*

Vanilla	bar	*42g*
	cup	*57g*
Viennetta, Walls	1 average size	*56g*

Woppa, Walls		*75g*

Zoom, Lyons Maid		*63g*

Milk products

Yoghurt

Yoghurt	1 tablespoon low fat	*50g*
	1 tablespoon thick/greek	*55g*

Yoghurt is generally purchased in cartons of 125g or 150g.
Examples of some common brands in each category are listed below.

125g pots

Chambourcy Le Yoghurt Low Fat Set (pack of 4)

Chambourcy Real Fruit Special Cultures (pack of 4)

Diary Crest Dennis The Menace

Dairy Crest Thick n Creamy

Dairy Crest Very Low Fat

Edenvale Diet Ski Very Low Fat Yoghurt with Vitamins (pack of 4)

Edenvale Natural Ski

Edenvale Munch Bunch (pack of 4)

Edenvale Munch Bunch Hi Juice Set Yoghurt (pack of 4)

Edenvale Munch Bunch Low Fat Yoghurt reduced sugar (pack of 4)

St Ivel Fiendish Feet

St Ivel Prize

St Ivel Real

St Ivel Shape Chunkier fruit Very Low Fat (pack of 4)

St Ivel Shape Set Very Low Fat Yoghurt (pack of 6)

Safeways Shapeline

Sainsburys Diet Yoghurt

Sainsburys Mr Men

Sainsburys French Recipe (pack of 4, 8)

Sainsburys Creamy Set Yoghurt (pack of 4)

Nouvelle Fruit Yoghurt

Bonjour Set Yoghurt

Chambourcy Le Yoghurt

Yoplait 100% Natural Yoghurt with real fruit (pack of 4)

Yoplait with real hazelnuts

150g pots	Edenvale Ski Low Fat Yoghurt with real fruit
	Edenvale Extra Fruit Ski Low Fat Yoghurt (pack of 4)
	Edenvale Gold Ski Thick and Creamy
	Country Love
	Sainsburys Natural Whole Milk
	Sainsburys Thick And Creamy
	Sainsburys Low Fat Fruit
	Boots Shapers
	Raines Low Fat Fruit
	Marks & Spencer Low Fat Fruit
	Marks & Spencer Lite
	Marks & Spencer Thick & Creamy
	Marks & Spencer Set Yoghurt
	Safeway Low Fat Fruit
	St Ivel Shape, natural
	Tesco Low Fat Fruit
	Tesco Thick and Creamy
	Loseley Low Fat Fruit
	Loseley Creamy
	Nature's Taste Set Yoghurt

Fruit Basket large yoghurts		*250g*
Total Greek yoghurt		*225g*
Yoghurt desserts	Edenvale Gold Ski Fruit Swirl	*150g*
	Muller Fruit corner—yoghurt portion	*135g*
	fruit portion	*40g*
	St Ivel Prize lightly whipped yoghurt	
	(pack of 4)	*90g*
	(singles)	*112g*

Milk products

MISCELLANEOUS AND BABY FOODS

Angelica	2 leaves	*1g*
Baby foods	Cow and Gate, stage 1 jars	*128g*
	stage 2 jars/yoghurts	*168g*
	ready to drink baby juice	*125g*
	Dried/powdered baby foods,	
	1 tablespoon	*15g*
	Heinz, tins or jars	*128g*
	Robinson's baby drinks, per carton	*250g*
	rusks, Boots, ruskmen	*8g*
	low sugar flavoured,	
	honey and apricot	*10g*
	Cow and Gate, Liga	*8g*
	Farex fingers	*9g*
	Farleys	*17g*
Baking powder	1 level teaspoon	*4g*
Bovril	see marmite	
Cherry	glace or maraschino, 1	*5g*
Curry powder	1 level teaspoon	*3g*
Glace cherry	1	*5g*
Gravy browning	1 teaspoon	*5g*
Herbs	dried, 1 teaspoon	*1g*
Hundreds and thousands	1 teaspoon	*4g*
Maraschino cherry	1	*5g*
Marmite, Bovril	thin scraping on bread	*1g*
	thick scraping on bread	*4g*
	1 heaped teaspoon	*18g*
	1 level teaspoon	*9g*

Miscellaneous

Mustard	1 level teaspoon	*8g*
	powder, 1 level teaspoon	*3g*
Oxo	stock cube, 1	*7g*
Parsley	dried, 1 level teaspoon	*1g*
	fresh, 1 large sprig	*1g*
Pepper	1 level teaspoon	*2g*
Salt	1 level teaspoon	*5g*
	1 heaped teaspoon	*8g*
Spices	dried, 1 teaspoon	*3g*
Stock cube	oxo, 1	*6g*
Stuffing	1 portion	*30g*
Vinegar	1 teaspoon	*5g*
	1 tablespoon	*15g*
Yeast extract	see Marmite	

Miscellaneous

NUTS AND SEEDS

Almonds	6 whole	*10g*
Brazil nuts	3 whole	*10g*
Cashew nuts	10 whole	*10g*
	roasted, salted, per bag	*25g*
Chestnuts	5 whole, peeled	*50g*
Cob nuts	hazelnuts, 10 whole	*10g*
Macademia nuts	6, no shell	*10g*
Mixed nuts and raisins	per bag, Big D, Percy Dalton	*30g*
	Golden Wonder	*40g*
	KP	*50g*
Monkey nuts	1 with shell	*2g*
Peanuts	10 whole	*10g*
	roasted, salted, per bag, small	*25g*
	medium	*40g*
	large	*100g*
Peanut butter	thickly spread on one slice	*20g*
	thinly spread on one slice	*12g*
Peanuts and raisins	1 handful	*40g*
Pecan nut	1, no shell	*6g*
Pistachio nuts	10, kernels only	*8g*
Sesame seeds	1 tablespoon	*10g*
Sesame seed spread	Tahini, 1 heaped teaspoon	*19g*
Sunflower seeds	1 tablespoon	*14g*

Tahini	1 heaped teaspoon	*19g*
Walnuts	6 halves	*20g*

PASTA, RICE AND GRAINS

Barley, pearl	boiled, 1 tablespoon	*20g*
	1 tablespoon dried, after boiling	*60g*
Bran	1 tablespoon	*7g*
Cornflour	1 heaped tablespoon	*30g*
Cous-cous	cracked wheat, average portion	*150g*
Custard powder	1 heaped tablespoon	*30g*
Dumpling, suet	1 average	*70g*
Flour	any, 1 level tablespoon	*20g*
	1 heaped tablespoon	*30g*
Macaroni	boiled, small average portion	*150g*
	medium	*230g*
	large	*350g*
Macaroni cheese	average portion	*300g*
	canned, average portion	*210g*
	large tin	*425g*
	small tin	*215g*
Noodles	instant, 1 packet, made up	*300g*
Oats	1 tablespoon	*15g*
Pasta	cooked, small average portion	*150g*
	medium average portion	*230g*
	large average portion	*350g*
	canned in tomato sauce, side dish	
	average portion	*125g*
	large tin	*425g*
	small tin	*215g*
Pot-noodles	as served	*300g*

Ravioli	average portion	*250g*
	canned, average portion	*200g*
	large tin	*410g*
	small tin	*230g*
Rice	boiled, average portion, small	*100g*
	medium	*150g*
	large	*200g*
	boiled/fried, take-away portion	*300g*
	pilau rice, per portion	*250g*
	salad, 1 tablespoon	*45g*
	savoury, average portion	*180g*
	1 packet made up	*300g*
Sago, semolina, tapioca pudding	average portion	*200g*
	canned, small can	*210g*
	large can	*430g*
Wheatgerm	1 tablespoon	*5g*

PUDDINGS AND FRUIT PIES

Apple crumble	(or any fruit) average portion	*170g*
Apple charlotte	average portion	*170g*
Apple danish	Mcdonalds	*100g*
Apple pie	see fruit pie	
	deep fried, Kentucky	*78g*
	deep fried, Mcdonalds	*90g*
	deep fried, Wimpy	*75g*
Arctic roll	average slice	*70g*
Bread pudding	average slice	*190g*
Blancmange	average portion	*150g*
Bread and butter pudding	average portion	*170g*
Cheesecake	average slice	*110g*
	individual	*100g*
Christmas pudding	average portion	*100g*
Creme caramel		*90g*
Crumble	any fruit, average portion	*170g*
Egg custard	average portion	*140g*
Custard	average portion	*150g*
	canned, half a can	*210g*
	cartoned, half a carton	*265g*
	ready to serve, per individual pot	*150g*
Fruit fool		*120g*

Fruit pie	average portion	*120g*
	deep fried, average portion	*80g*
	individual, small	*50g*
	individual, large	*100g*
	half large purchased pie	*150g*
Fruit sponge	average portion	*170g*
Fruit sundae	individual	*100g*
Instant whip	Angel Delight, average portion	*120g*
	purchased, ready to eat	*100g*
Jelly	average portion	*200g*
Milk puddings	average	*200g*
	canned large	*434g*
	small	*210g*
Mousse	purchased frozen, individual, average	*60g*
	purchased, individual, average	*60g*
Pancakes	small	*60g*
	medium	*110g*
	large	*150g*
Pavlova		*150g*
Rice pudding	see milk puddings	
Souffle		*113g*
Sponge pudding	canned, whole	*300g*
	average portion	*170g*
	purchased, individual	*100g*
Suet pudding	average portion	*150g*
Trifle	home made	*170g*
	individual purchased	*113g*

Puddings

Viennetta	one quarter	*45g*
Waffle, sweet		*65g*
General puddings	small	*120g*
	medium	*150g*
	large	*180g*

Puddings

SAUCES, PICKLES AND SOUPS

Apple sauce	average portion	*20g*
Blue cheese dressing	1 tablespoon	*25g*
Bread sauce	average portion	*45g*
Brown sauce	1 sachet	*30g*
Cheese sauce	with meat/fish/vegetables,	
	small portion	*30g*
	medium portion	*60g*
	large portion	*90g*
Cranberry sauce	average portion	*30g*
Curry sauce	average portion	*115g*
French dressing	1 salad, average portion	*15g*
Gravy	small average portion	*45g*
	medium average portion	*70g*
	large average portion	*120g*
Mayonnaise	with salad average portion	*30g*
	1 tablespoon	*33g*
Mint jelly	average portion	*20g*
Mint sauce	average portion	*10g*
Mustard	average portion, smooth type	*2g*
	average portion, whole grain type	*14g*
Onion sauce	average portion	*60g*
Pickle	with ploughmans, average portion	*40g*
	1 heaped teaspoon	*15g*
Pickled beetroot	1 average	*35g*

Pickled cabbage	1 tablespoon	*45g*
Pickled gherkin	1 small	*8g*
	1 medium	*25g*
	1 large, pickled cucumber	*60g*
Pickled onion	1 average	*10g*
	1 large	*25g*
	1 silverskin onion	*2g*
Prawn cocktail sauce	average	*40g*
Relish	in burger	*15g*
	1 heaped teaspoon	*15g*
Salad cream	average with salad	*30g*
Savoury sauces	see white sauce	
Soup	small average portion	*150g*
	medium average portion	*220g*
	large average portion	*300g*
	cup-a-soup, made up	*210g*
	large tin	*425g*
	small tin	*290g*
	vending machine soup	*170g*
Soy sauce	1 teaspoon	*5g*
Sweet 'n' sour sauce	average portion	*150g*
Tartare sauce	average serving	*30g*
Thousand island dressing	1 tablespoon	*30g*
Tomato ketchup	1 sachet/average serving	*30g*
Tomato sauce	average with meat/fish/pasta	*90g*
White sauce	with meat/fish/vegetables, small	*30g*
	medium	*60g*
	large	*90g*

SAVOURY SNACKS

All weights given per bag

Alien Spacers		*26g*
Bombay mix	Sharwoods	*100g*
	Golden Glow	*28g*
Bran Krisps		*30g*
Californian Corn Chips		*100g*
Cheesey Crunchies		*18g*
Cheese Quavers		*20g*
Cheesey Moments		*28g*
Cheese Snips		*30g*
Cheezers		*26g*
Chickbits		*27g*
Chicken Wickers		*23g*
Chipsletten		*100g*
Country Crunch		*18g*
Crackles		*18g*
Crisps	small	*25/28/30g*
	medium	*40g*
	large	*75g*
Crispy Tubes		*25g*
Crunchy Bumpkins		*16g*
Discos		*18g/29g*
Frazzles		*27g*
Good 'n' Crunchy Crisps		*35g*
Groovers		*30g*
Hula Hoops		*30g*
Jackets		*28g*
Japanese Rice Crackers		*56g*
Java Crackers		*40g*
Jaws		*28g*
McCoys		*40g*
Mexican Chips		*30g*

Mignons Morceau		*100g*
Monster Munch		*27g*
Nature's Choice		*27g*
Nature's Snack	wholewheat crisps	*20g*
Nik-Naks		*35g*
Odduns		*26g*
Pizza Biscuits		*30g*
Porky Scratchings		*22g*
Potato Waffles		*40g*
Prawn Crackers	Chinese take-away	*70g*
Preludes		*75g*
Quavers		*20g*
Real McCoys		*40g*
Ringos		*24g*
Ritz Sandwich, 4		*33g*
Rounders		*34g*
Scampi Fries		*28g*
Sky Divers		*18g*
Skips		*18g*
Spicy Popadums		*30g*
Square Crisps		*28g*
Stackers		*100g*
Stix		*24g*
Supasnax	cheese flavoured corn curls	*13/24g*
Superheroes		*24g*
Tortilla Chips		*100g*
Twiglets		*50g*
Twists		*25g*
Wheateats		*25g*
Wheatsticks		*60g*
Wotsits		*25g*

NB Most supermarkets sell crisps and snacks in large bags of 50–100g.

SUGARS, PRESERVES AND SWEET SAUCES

Brandy sauce, rum sauce	average portion	*60g*
Brandy butter	average portion	*30g*
Cherry	glace or maraschino, 1	*5g*
Chocolate sauce	average portion	*60g*
Chocolate spread	1 average spreading on 1 slice of bread	*20g*
	1 heaped teaspoon	*16g*
	1 level teaspoon	*8g*
Honey	1 average spreading on 1 slice of bread	*20g*
	1 heaped teaspoon	*17g*
	1 level teaspoon	*8g*
Ice-cream topping sauce	average topping	*15g*
Jam, marmalade, lemon curd	1 average spreading on 1 slice bread	*15g*
	1 heaped teaspoon	*18g*
	1 individual carton	*25g*
	1 level teaspoon	*8g*
Maple syrup	serving on waffles	*55g*
Marmalade	see jam	
Sugar	1 cube	*5g*
	1 heaped teaspoon	*6g*
	1 level teaspoon	*4g*
	1 'packet' sugar	*7g*
	1 tablespoon	*20g*

VEGETABLES

Artichoke	one globe heart, edible portion	50g
Asparagus	5 spears	125g
Aubergine	half including skin, cooked	130g
Baked beans	in tomato sauce, small portion	80g
	medium portion	135g
	large portion	190g
	1 small tin	225g
	1 large tin	450g
	1 tablespoon	45g
	with sausage, small tin, beans	170g
	sausage	55g
	large tin, beans	305g
	sausage	145g
	with burgerbites, chickbits, small tin,	
	beans	170g
	burgerbites/chickbits	55g
Beanburger	Wimpy, with bun	236g
Beans	broad 2 tablespoons	120g
	french small portion	60g
	medium portion	90g
	large portion	120g
	dried, boiled, two tablespoons	60g
	red kidney, 1 heaped tablespoon	
	cooked beans	30g
	runner, small portion	60g
	medium portion	90g
	large portion	120g
Beansprouts	1 tablespoon	20g
Beetroot	1 small whole	35g
	per slice	10g
Bhindi	see okra	

Broccoli spears	calabrese, 1 boiled	45g
Brussels sprouts	average serving, 9 sprouts	90g
	small portion	60g
	medium portion	90g
	large portion	120g
Bubble and squeak	fried, average portion	200g
Cabbage, boiled	any, small portion	60g
	medium portion	90g
	large portion	120g
	red/white, raw, 1/6 small cabbage	90g
Calabrese	1 spear	45g
Carrots	boiled, small portion	40g
	medium portion	60g
	large portion	85g
	canned, 1 medium carrot	12g
	1 medium, boiled	45g
	a few slices	20g
	a tablespoon	40g
Cauliflower	1 floret	10g
	small portion	60g
	medium portion	90g
	large portion	120g
	Bhaji	140g
	cheese see cheese dishes	
Celery	1 stick	30g
	boiled, small portion	30g
	medium portion	50g
	large portion	80g
Chick peas	1 heaped tablespoon cooked peas	28g
	2–3 tablespoons, cooked	90g
	paste, hummous, 1 tablespoon	30g
	1 heaped tablespoon	55g

Vegetables

Chinese leaves	1 large leaf	*40g*
Chips	see potato chips	
Coleslaw	1 tablespoon	*45g*
	1 large tub	*224g*
	Take-away portion, Kentucky	*100g*
Corn-on-the-cob	see sweetcorn	
Courgettes	1 large cooked	*100g*
	small portion	*60g*
	medium portion	*90g*
	large portion	*120g*
Cress	see mustard and cress	
Cucumber	1 slice	*6g*
	1″ piece	*60g*
	average in salad	*23g*
French fries	see potato chips	
Green banana	1 whole boiled	*140g*
Leek	1 medium, boiled	*160g*
	stem, white portion only	*80g*
Lentils	boiled, 1 tablespoon	*30g*
	boiled (2oz raw)	*120g*
Lettuce	4 small leaves	*20g*
	round, average serving in salad	*30g*
	iceberg, average serving in salad	*80g*
Marrow	average serving	*224g*
Mixed vegetables	average serving	*90g*
Mushrooms	raw, 1 average	*10g*
	fried, average serving	*44g*

Mustard and cress	1 tablespoon	*5g*
	in sandwich	*2g*
	quarter of a punnet	*10g*
Okra	ladies fingers, bindi, 1 medium	*5g*
	bhindi bhaji,	
	okra curry	*250g*
Onion	raw, 1 average	*90g*
	1 slice	*20g*
	boiled, average serving	*60g*
	fried, average serving	*57g*
	bhaji, fried, 1 average	*60g*
	rings, battered, average portion	*85g*
	pickled, 1 average	*10g*
	1 large	*25g*
	spring, 1	*20g*
Parsnips	average portion, small	*40g*
	medium	*65g*
	large	*85g*
	1 medium baked	*90g*
Peas	average portion, small	*40g*
	medium	*65g*
	large	*85g*
	mushy, average portion	*85g*
	mushy, fish and chip shop, average	
	portion	*125g*
	tinned, 1 tablespoon	*30g*
Pepper	green or red, 1 medium	*160g*
	sliced, 1 ring	*10g*
	half a stuffed pepper	*175g*
Plantain	1 whole, boiled	*200g*
Potatoes	baked, jacket, small with skin	*100g*
	without skin	*88g*
	medium, with skin	*180g*
	without skin	*160g*
	large, with skin	*220g*
	without skin	*195g*

Vegetables

Potatoes, *continued*

boiled, 1 average old potato	*60g*
1 average new potato	*40g*
1 average portion, small	*120g*
medium	*180g*
large	*220g*
cakes, fried, each	*80g*
chips, 1 chip	*10g*
chips, average portions, small	*130g*
medium	*180g*
large	*240g*
average portion fish and chip shop chips	*200g*
average portion "french fries"	*100g*
Kentucky, french fries, regular	*112g*
large	*168g*
Mcdonalds, french fries, regular	*93g*
large	*124g*
Wimpy, french fries	*100g*
crisps, 1 average bag	*25g*
1 large crisp	*2g*
See also savoury snacks	
croquette, fried, 1 average	*90g*
grilled, 1 average	*80g*
crunchies, fried, 1	*9g*
grilled, 1	*6g*
average portion	*90g*
duchesse, 1	*30g*
fritter, 1	*120g*
mashed, portions as boiled	
1 tablespoon	*45g*
1 scoop	*60g*
1 forkful	*30g*
pancakes, baked/grilled	*50g*
fried	*56g*
roast, 1 small potato	*50g*
1 medium potato	*85g*
1 large potato	*130g*
average portion	*200g*
salad, 1 tablespoon	*45g*
1 small tub	*112g*
saute, average portion	*100g*
scallops, average portion	*150g*

Potatoes, *continued*	waffles, 1 grilled	*45g*
Radish	1 average	*8g*
Ratatouille	1 tablespoon	*30g*
Sauerkraut	1 tablespoon	*30g*
Spinach	average serving	*90g*
Spring Roll	average, fried	*85g*
Swede	boiled, small portion	*40g*
	medium portion	*60g*
	large portion	*85g*
Sweetcorn	kernels only, 1 tablespoon	*30g*
	1 Corn-on-the-Cob, kernels only	*125g*
	fritter, 1	*85g*
Sweet potatoes	boiled, 2 medium	*130g*
Tomato	1 small	*65g*
	1 medium	*85g*
	1 large eg beefsteak tomato	*150g*
	1 slice	*17g*
	1 cherry tomato	*15g*
	average in salad	*34g*
Turnip	boiled see Swede	
	1 whole boiled	*110g*
Vegeburger	average, fried	*56g*
Vegetable salad	in mayonnaise, 1 tablespoon	*45g*
Vegetable curry	1 serving, 2–3 tablespoons	*200g*
Watercress	quarter of a bunch	*20g*
Yam	boiled, size of a medium potato	*130g*

Vegetables